Céad Míle Fáilte to the 2016 edition of Ireland's Blue Book

Welcome, fáilte, bienvenue, willkommen, benvenuto, bienvenida, 欢迎, ようこそ

Welcome to the 2016 edition of Ireland's Blue Book. We are a unique association comprising the country's finest country manor houses, historic hotels, castles and restaurants. No two properties are the same, each offering an enchanting and unique atmosphere.

If you are looking for a gourmet getaway or seeking a scenic retreat there is somewhere perfect for you in the Blue Book. For those desiring a more active break we have fishing, golf, cycling and equestrian pursuits. Included in our collection are some indulgent spas for those looking to be spoiled. Or perhaps combine business with pleasure and book your corporate event with us.

We look forward to welcoming you in 2016.

Sallyanne Clarke
Sallyanne Clarke
President of Ireland's Blue Book

D09866669

IRISCHE LANDHÄUSER UND RESTAURANTS

Hinter dem Namen **Ireland's Blue Book** verbirgt sich ein exklusiver Zusammenschluss irischer Gastbetriebe, die in einzigartigen Land- und Herrenhäusern, Schlössern und Gourmetrestaurants untergebracht sind. Die Häuser der Blue Book- Mitglieder sind ideal für den anspruchsvollen Gast und bieten traditionelle irische Gastfreundschaft, erstklassige Unterbringung und Gourmetküche inmitten der anmutigen Schönheit der ländlichen Idylle Irlands.

CASAS DE CAMPO Y RESTAURANTES DE IRLANDA

Ireland's Blue Book es un exclusivo Grupo que reúne a las principales casas solariegas, hoteles históricos, castillos y restaurantes de Irlanda. Los establecimientos que se presentan en el Blue Book colmarán las expectativas de los visitantes más exigentes, atraídos por la serena belleza de la Irlanda rural ya sea en busca de hospitalidad tradicional, alojamiento o gastronomía de calidad.

RISTORANTI E DIMORE DI CAMPAGNA IRLANDESI

Ireland's Blue Book è un'associazione esclusiva che riunisce le dimore di campagna, gli hotel storici, i castelli e i ristoranti più belli del paese. Gli edifici descritti nel Blue Book non potranno fare a meno di attirare l'attenzione dei visitatori più esigenti in cerca di accoglienza tradizionale, ospitalità dagli standard elevati e cucina squisita nella serena bellezza della campagna irlandese.

RELAIS DE CAMPAGNE ET RESTAURANTS D'IRLANDE

Ireland's Blue Book est une association exceptionnelle qui rassemble les plus beaux manoirs, hôtels à caractère historique, châteaux et restaurants du pays. Les établissements présentés dans le Blue Book séduiront les visiteurs exigeants, à la recherche d'une hospitalité traditionnelle et raffinée, d'un hébergement de qualité et d'une cuisine savoureuse, au coeur de la beauté paisible d'une Irlande rurale.

魅力的なカントリーハウス・ホテルとレストラン

「アイルランド・ブルーブック」には、アイルランドで指折りのカントリー・ハウス、城、レストランが加盟しています。静かで美しいアイルランドの自然のなかで、伝統的に名高いアイルランド流「おもてなし」が体験できる、宿泊施設、レストランをお探しの方に、最適の場をご紹介しています。

HOW TO BOOK A BLUE BOOK HOUSE

Simply visit Ireland's Blue Book website and make your
reservation/booking.

www.irelandsbluebook.com

Perhaps you are more comfortable dealing with a person rather than
booking online. In this instance please contact the houses directly;
they would love to hear from you. At the bottom of each page you
will find the proprietor's name, address, telephone, email and website.

Reservations can also be made through your travel agent.

Reservation Agents in North America and Canada, please call

USA/Canada Toll Free 800 323 5463

Contact details
Ireland's Blue Book
63 Fitzwilliam Square
Dublin 2, Ireland

T +353 (0) 1 676 9914
USA/Canada Toll Free 800 323 5463
E mail@irelandsbluebook.com
www.irelandsbluebook.com

AHERNE'S TOWNHOUSE LUXURY INN & SEAFOOD RESTAURANT

Open fires and the warmest of welcomes await you in this family run hotel in the historic walled port of Youghal. Rooms are spacious and stylishly furnished. The famous Seafood Bar and Restaurant specialises in the freshest of Seafood (Lobster, Oysters, Crab, Prawns, Black Sole, Monkfish & Turbot) our bar is renowned for its friendliness; you can enjoy a chat with the locals along with your Guinness and Seafood. Gluten-free meals served for 30 years. Available for Intimate Weddings /Private Parties. Civil Marriage approved.

Local attractions: Walking, Swimming, Seaweed Baths, Horse Riding, Golfing, Sea Angling, Kayaking, Greyhound Racing, Jameson Heritage Centre, Fota Wildlife Park, Ardmore Cliff Walk, Blarney Castle, Waterford Crystal and Lismore Castle.

Awards include:
Listed in the country's **top 20 best Pubs in Hot Press** Best of Ireland 2014
Guardian Newspaper – 'One of the best breakfasts in Ireland'

A Blue Book Voucher – complimentary upgrade where possible.

Bedrooms **12**   Guesthouse ★ ★ ★ ★

Aherne's, 163 North Main Street, Youghal, Co.Cork
T +353 (0)24 92424
F +353 (0)24 93633
info@ahernes.net
www.ahernes.com

Proprietor: The FitzGibbon Family
Open all year – except 4 days at Christmas.
Bed & Breakfast from €55 – €120 pps.
Single from €80 – €120.
Dinner 6.00pm to 9.30pm from €30.00.
Bar Food Service available Noon – 10pm daily.
Guide dogs welcome.
Small dogs by arrangement.

How to find:
Cork: 30 mins. (N25) Direction Rosslare.
Rosslare: 1.45hrs (N25).
Dublin: Take the N7 then the M7 onto the M9 to Waterford then take the N25 West to Youghal. 2.30hrs.

GPS coordinates
Lat: 51.957031634671
Long: -7.8518871130346

ARDTARA

Ardtara is an elegantly restored 19th century mansion, **situated at the centre of Northern Ireland within 45 minutes of the North Antrim Coast, the Giant's Causeway, Derry/Londonderry and Belfast.**

In fact, every scenic attraction in Northern Ireland north of Belfast, plus all airports and Royal Portrush links golf are all within 60 minutes.

Ardtara is honoured to be included in *National Geographic Traveler Magazine's* **'Best Places to Stay in Britain and Ireland'** and has been named **'Most Romantic Hotel of the Year'** by the AA.

Ardtara offers en-suite bedrooms with king beds, owner-collected antiques and original working fireplaces, within the privacy of eight wooded acres.

Recent Awards:
"Best Hotel Restaurant in Ulster 2015"
"Best Emerging Cuisine in Ulster 2015"
(Irish Restaurants Association).

Bedrooms **9**   **Listed Heritage Property**

**Ardtara Country House & Restaurant,
8 Gorteade Road, Upperlands,
Co. L'Derry BT46 5SA**
T +44 (0)28 796 44490
info@ardtara.com
www.ardtara.com

Proprietors: Roulston & Orr Families
Bed & Full Irish Breakfast from £49.50 – £70 pps.
Dinners & Sunday lunch available to all by reservation.
Dinner 5.30pm – 9.30pm à la carte.
Private Dining Room available by reservation.
Complimentary Wi-Fi on ground floor.

How to find:
Take M2/M22/A6 north toward Derry/Londonderry.
7 miles past the Castledawson roundabout, take A29 through Maghera. Continue on A29 towards Coleraine for three miles out of Maghera to the right turn on to B75. Proceed one mile into Upperlands. Ardtara sign is on the left towards the end of the village.

GPS coordinates
N 54.88297
W -6.636611

Family-run country house famous for outstanding hospitality & superb food. Produce is locally sourced & from the farm.

17th century house built on a Norman keep nestled in 300-acre estate in rural East Cork. Located minutes from the coast and twenty miles from the historic city of Cork. Bedrooms range from elegant & airy to charming & cosy.

Facilities include a small golf course, tennis court, summer swimming pool & croquet lawn. The Ballymaloe Cookery School is nearby and on site The Grainstore is an ideal venue for conferences & weddings & hosts many cultural events year-round.

2015 Awards:
Condé Nast Traveller "Gold list 100 World's Best Hotels"
Food & Wine "Ireland's Top restaurants"
Georgina Campbell "Best breakfasts in Ireland"

Bedrooms **29**   Guesthouse ★ ★ ★ ★

Ballymaloe House, Shanagarry, Co.Cork
T +353 (0)21 465 2531
F +353 (0)21 465 2021
res@ballymaloe.ie
www.ballymaloe.ie

Proprietor: The Allen Family
Closed 24, 25, 26 December. 8 Jan. – 8 Feb.
Bed & Breakfast per person sharing.
Low season €100 – €120
High season €120 – €150.
Service charge optional.
Dinner €75, from 7.00 – 9.30pm.
All major credit cards accepted.
Children welcome.

How to find:
From Cork take N25 east. Then take R630 and R631. We are two miles beyond Cloyne on the Ballycotton road. From Waterford take N25 west to Castlemartyr. In Ladysbridge take care to follow signs to Cloyne, we are two miles from Ladysbridge on the Cloyne Road.

GPS coordinates
N 5551.88 W 00804.50
2.29 SSW Castlemartyr

BARBERSTOWN CASTLE

Formerly the home of Eric Clapton and welcoming visitors for over 800 years, visitors to Barberstown will experience a very relaxing and welcoming Castle while enjoying great food, good wines, open log fires, luxury and exceptional personal service.

Use this unique Historic 13th Century Irish Castle as the ideal base from which to visit Dublin and the East Coast of Ireland. Enjoy 30 minutes carefree driving from or to Dublin Airport and 30 minutes from all the sites to visit in Dublin City Centre.

Essential Day Trips for your Vacation – Irish National Stud and Japanese Gardens. Drive to the Garden of Ireland in Wicklow visiting Russborough, Glendalough and Powerscourt. Newgrange (5,000 year old Megalithic site) and The Rock of Cashel are great day trips.

Awards include:
Best Historic Hotel of Europe CASTLE 2014 award

Bedrooms **55 Ensuite**   Hotel ★ ★ ★ ★

Barberstown Castle, Straffan, Co.Kildare
T +353 (0)1 628 8157
F +353 (0)1 627 7027
info@barberstowncastle.ie
www.barberstowncastle.ie

Proprietor: Kenneth Healy
Open all year except three days Christmas, January and February
Bed & Breakfast Rates: €75 – €125 pps and €52.00 single room supplement.
Dinner: Table d'Hôte Menu available 6 – 8:30pm.
Lunch: Tea Rooms open daily 12 – 5pm.

GDS Codes:
HE DUBBCH, HE 29023, HE 30473, HE DUBBC

How to find:
Leave the airport and take the exit for the M50 South Bound. Leave the M50 at exit #7 (M4) and continue on the N4/M4 westward. Leave the M4 at Exit/Junction 7 (Straffan/Maynooth) and take the R407 to Straffan. (30 minutes - all Motorway).
Onward Journey: Because the Castle is minutes from the M1, M50, M4 and M7 motorways, it is the most perfect starting point, or final evening, on your Blue Book tour of Ireland. This Castle is easy to Find but hard to Leave!

5

In this Georgian country house standing at the head of Dunmanus Bay everything revolves around the courtyard. Finely restored with cobbled paths, shrubs and flowers its 500 year old stone outbuildings contain four beautiful apartments as well as the restaurant with its magnificent dining room.

Blairscove Restaurant is best known for its buffet style starters and scrumptious desserts.

The elegant setting, the pretty courtyard and the landscaped gardens make it an ideal venue for weddings of up to 100 guests.

AA 2 rosettes 2015.
One Fab Day 100 best wedding venues 2015.
Tripadvisor certificate of Excellence 2015
Michelin Guide 2015
AA****Gold Star Awards 2015 Restaurant with rooms
Georgina Campbells Ireland Guide 'Outstanding Guest Experience of the year 2015'
Irish Design 2015
National Hospitality Awards 2014: Best Dining Experience

Bedrooms **4 courtyard suites, 1 cottage in the grounds**

Blairscove House, Durrus near Bantry, Co.Cork
T +353 (0)27 61127
mail@blairscove.ie
www.blairscove.ie

Proprietors: The De Mey family
Restaurant: Open from March 17
to October 29 2016
Tuesday to Saturday 6:30 to 9:30PM
3 course table d'hôte menu €60
Accommodation: Open from March 17 to
October 29 2016.
Bed & Breakfast €75 – €130 mid-week.
Friday and Saturday €110 – €130.
Single supplement €30.
Self catering cottage available.
Major credit cards accepted.

How to find: Coming from Durrus follow the R591 to Crook haven. After 1.5 miles you'll see the blue gate on the right hand side.
Cork airport: 1 hr 15 mins.

GPS coordinates
51 degrees 36' 33" N
9 degrees 32' 18" W

BROWNS RESTAURANT & CHAMPAGNE LOUNGE

Since rebirth in 2009, "Browns Restaurant" has gained a reputation for excellent food, genuine hospitality and great service. The critics have not only established this multi-award winning restaurant as the best in the North West but have placed it among the best in Ireland.

Located in the heart of the iconic city of Derry and overlooking the River Foyle, Browns with its Art Deco interior is the sister restaurant to Ardtara Country House.

Chef Patron Ian Orr, driven by his passion for great local produce and seasonality is tipped as one of Ireland's top talents and the awards and critical acclaim have flowed over the years:

Restaurants Association of Ireland	Best Restaurant in Northern Ireland 2013 Best Restaurant in Co. Derry every year since 2010
Michelin Guide	Recommended
Georgina Campbell	Ireland's Chef of the Year 2013

Covers **70**

Browns Restaurant & Champagne Lounge, 1 Bonds Hill Derry/Londonderry, BT47 6DW
T +44 (0)28 7134 5180
eat@brownsrestaurant.com
www.brownsrestaurant.com

Proprietors: Ian Orr & Marcus Roulston
Opening Hours:
Lunch: Tuesday-Friday	12:00pm-3:00pm
Sunday lunch:	12:00pm-3:30pm
Dinner: Tuesday-Thursday	5:30pm-9:00pm
Dinner: Friday-Saturday	5:00pm-10:00pm

Lunch Menu 3 courses:	£15
Dinner set menu 3 courses:	£21.95
Dinner a la carte 3 courses:	from £30

How to find: Browns Restaurant is located on the east side of Lough Foyle just off the A2 at the junction of A2 and Bonds Hill.

GPS coordinates
54.993418
-7.312089

BUSHMILLS INN HOTEL

The Bushmills Inn is situated in an enviable location a stone's throw from Royal Portrush Golf Club, The Giant's Causeway and Dunluce Castle. Roaring peat fires, nooks and crannies and a secret library set the tone.

In the bar, still lit by gas light, try a glass of malt from the hotel's private cask and sample the finest North Antrim produce in the AA Rosette restaurant.

Whether you wish to linger by the fire, enjoy afternoon tea on the garden courtyard, partake in water sports, hike in unspoilt countryside or play golf on some of Ireland's finest courses Bushmills Inn is the ideal location.

Awards include:

AA Hotel of the Year for Northern Ireland 2014-2015

Northern Ireland Tourism Awards Hotel of the Year 2015

YesChef Best Regional Restaurant 2015 (Ulster)

TripAdvisor 2015 Hall of Fame (Five-time Certificate of Excellence Winner)

Bedrooms **41**   Specialist accommodation **Historic Building**   Hotel ★ ★ ★ ★

Bushmills Inn Hotel, 9 Dunluce Road, Bushmills, Co.Antrim, BT57 8QG
T + 44(0)28 207 33000
mail@bushmillsinn.com
www.bushmillsinn.com

Proprietor: Alan Dunlop
Hotel Manager: Alan Walls
Open all year Monday to Sunday.
Restaurant open all day: 12 noon to 9.30,
dinner 6pm to 9.30pm Stg£30.
B&B: Low Season: Oct – Mar from £65 pps
High Season: April – Sept from £90 pps
All bedrooms non-smoking.
Credit Cards: Amex, Mastercard, Visa.

How to find:
From Belfast follow the M2 north to Ballymena then A26 to Ballymoney. At the roundabout take the third exit onto B62 heading to Portrush/Bushmills, turn right onto Priestland Road (B17) then right onto Dunluce Road (A2). The Bushmills Inn will be on the left.

GPS coordinates
N 55 12' 25.64"
W 6 31' 26.63"

CAMPAGNE RESTAURANT

Campagne restaurant in Kilkenny city opened in 2008. The emphasis has been to serve food based on high-quality seasonal produce with French influences in a relaxed and comfortable dining area.

Located under the old railway arches on Gas House Lane, Campagne boasts a stylish interior featuring oak flooring, curved banquette leather seating and modern paintings depicting rural life by Kilkenny artist Catherine Barron.

Campagne has been awarded many prestigious awards on a national and international level, most notably one Michelin star status in September 2013.

At Campagne we have a passionately held philosophy that supports and showcases the very best of quality food and wine producers.

Campagne Restaurant
5 The Arches, Gas House Lane, Kilkenny
T +353 (0)56 777 2858
info@campagne.ie   www.campagne.ie

Proprietors: Garrett Byrne & Brid Hannon
Opening hours:
Closed Sunday nights and all day Monday
Lunch: Friday and Saturday 12.30pm – 2.30pm
Sunday Lunch: 12.30pm – 3.00pm
Early Bird: Tuesday – Thursday 6pm – 7pm
(5.30pm – 6pm on Fridays and Saturdays)
Dinner: Tuesday – Saturday 6pm – 10pm,
Open Sunday nights on Bank Holidays, closed on
Tuesday nights following Bank Holiday.
Annual Holidays: Last two weeks in January and
first week in July.

How to find:
Campagne is located just under the cities old railway arches, in an area called John's green, the restaurant is in close proximity to Mc Donagh Junction shopping centre.

GPS coordinates
52°8304;39'21" N
7°8304;14'47" W

Hidden away on the shores of Caragh Lake, Ring of Kerry, enchanting 'Carrig' offers an 'escape from it all' and the most beautiful scenery in Ireland.

Enjoy golf, fishing, horse riding or hiking. Tour the Ring of Kerry, Dingle Peninsula, Killarney National Park or World Heritage Site Skellig Michael.

Snuggle up in a comfy king size bed and awake to the sound of the lake lapping on the shore. Stroll the wonderful gardens (950 species) or indulge in a good book or game of chess in the spacious Drawing Rooms.

Savour fine wines and mouth-watering Irish Country House cooking in our award winning **Lakeside Restaurant**.

Frank, Mary and Team extend a warm welcome and unique Irish Country House experience.

Georgina Campbell's Ireland Guide: 'Country House of the Year' 2013
Good Hotel Guide Editors Choice
Irish Restaurant Awards Best Chef in Kerry 2015.

Bedrooms **17** Suites **2**   Country House ★ ★ ★ ★

Carrig Country House & Restaurant,
Caragh Lake, Killorglin, Co.Kerry V93 WK83
T +353 (0)66 976 9100
info@carrighouse.com www.carrighouse.com

Hosts / Proprietors: Frank & Mary Slattery
Closed November – February inclusive
Bed & breakfast per person sharing:
€75 – €155 pps Low Season
€90 – €190 pps High Season
Single supplement €55
2 & 3 Day Value Package price on
www.carrighouse.com
Dinner: from €49.50 per person from 7 – 9pm.
A La Carte also available
Visa, Mastercard, Maestro Accepted
Children over the age of 8 years are welcome.

How to find:
From Killorglin (10 minutes) – N70 from Killorglin towards Glenbeigh for 4km. After PROMED offices, take 2nd left for Caragh Lake (signposted). At Caragh Lake School and Shop see signpost for Carrig, take sharp right, located 1km further on the left.
From Glenbeigh (10 minutes) – Take the N70 in the direction of Killorglin for 4km, go over one-way stone bridge turning right, continue for approx. 1km and turn right onto the Caragh Lake road (Carrig signpost, before the Red Fox Inn) and drive for 2km. Carrig Country House is on the right.

GPS coordinates
N 52 4' 26.23"
W 9 51' 0.58"

CASHEL HOUSE HOTEL

A perfect start of your adventure on the Wild Atlantic Way – Cashel House formerly one of Connemara's most gracious homes, set in 50 acres of magnificent gardens on the beautiful coastline of Cashel Bay with Cashel Hill rising behind.

Owned by the McEvilly Family for 50 years, where a warm welcome awaits you. Relax in our Drawing Room with open log fires, antiques and fine arts. Retire to comfortable bedrooms all individually decorated or dine in our restaurant overlooking the garden which serves the finest local seafood and meat dishes with vegetables from our garden and region.

Enjoy walking, beaches, sea and lake fishing, riding, hiking, golf, Connemara ponies in our stud farm, visit to Kylemore Gardens, travel to Aran and Inish Boffin islands or take a boat trip off Killary Fjord.

Bedrooms **16**   Suites **13**   Hotel ★ ★ ★ ★

**Cashel House Hotel, Cashel,
Connemara, Co.Galway, H91 XE10**
T +353 (0)95 31001
sales@cashelhouse.ie
www.cashelhouse.ie

Proprietors: The McEvilly Family
Closed January and reopen on 11 February.
Bed & Breakfast per person sharing
€75 – €165 pps Low Season
€80 – €190 pps High Season
Children welcome
Special Breaks on request
Dinner: 3 course €32.00, 5 course €55.00,
A la Carte also available
All major credit cards accepted

Pet friendly
Exclusive wedding parties 120 max
Gratuity at your discretion.

How to find:
South off N59 (Galway Clifden Road).
1.6 kilometres (1 mile) west of Recess, turn left.

GPS coordinates
53.419547
-9.807950

CASTLE DURROW

COUNTRY HOUSE & RESTAURANT

Built by Viscount Ashbrook in 1716, in the picturesque village of Durrow, Co.Laois conveniently located about 1 hour from Dublin and 1.5 hours from Cork. Lovingly restored and family home to Peter and Shelly Stokes, Castle Durrow is now one of Ireland's magnificent luxury four star hotels and proudly one of Ireland's most popular wedding venues.

Explore the estate, the surrounding woodlands and river pathways or stroll through our amazing gardens where lots of our organic kitchen produce is grown. Visit the Cafes, Bars, Restaurants and Shops of Durrow, the nearby Heritage Town of Abbeyleix and surrounding historic sites at Kilkenny Castle and Rock of Cashel both 30 mins.

TripAdvisor – Top 10 Castle Hotels of the World, Hall of Fame winner 2015.
Irish Restaurant Association Awards Winner – 2010 up to and including 2015.
One Fab Day – Top 100 wedding Venues in Ireland.

Bedrooms **46 and quirky Gate Lodge**

Castle Durrow, Durrow, Co.Laois
T +353 (0)57 873 6555
F +353 (0)57 873 6559
info@castledurrow.com
www.castledurrow.com
www.facebook.com/CastleDurrow

Proprietors: The Stokes Family
Open all year but closed for Christmas
24–26 December inc
Restaurant Open Wednesday – Sunday
Dinner, Bed & Breakfast from €195 - €250 per couple
Four Course Dinner from €37.50 per person
Sunday Lunch from €27.50 per person
Private Dining Rooms available for special occasions

How to find:
From Dublin: On M7 take exit 17 then N77 through Abbeyleix to Durrow.
From Cork: On M8 take exit 4 then R639 through Johnstown, Cullohill to Durrow.

GPS Coordinates:
Lat: 52.846301
Long: -7.401223

CASTLE LESLIE ESTATE

Steeped in history, full of character and charm, Castle Leslie Estate is the ultimate Irish rural escape. Nestled on 1,000 acres of undulating Irish countryside, dotted with ancient woodland and glittering lakes, Castle Leslie Estate, is one of the last great Irish castle estates still in the hands of its founding family.

The Castle, at the heart of the Estate, offers authentic original interiors and old-style hospitality.

The Lodge, our country house style boutique hotel has 29 rooms – each of which remain true to the building's original structure. Explore the Estate on horseback, enjoy some of Ireland's finest coarse fishing, luxuriate in a relaxing massage or just a stroll through the woods – just some of the choices that await you in this hidden corner of Ireland.

Hotel and Catering Review Gold Medal Award 2015:
Best Hotel Breakfast – The Castle at Castle Leslie
AA Courtesy and Care Award 2015 – 2016:
The Lodge at Castle Leslie Estate

Bedrooms **49**   Specialist accommodation **Historic Castle**

Castle Leslie Estate, Glaslough, Co.Monaghan
T +353 (0)47 88100
info@castleleslie.com
www.castleleslie.com

Proprietor: Sammy Leslie
General Manager: Brian Baldwin
From €95 pps, bed and breakfast
Single occupancy from €170 bed and breakfast.

How to find:
From Dublin take M1 north. Exit at Junction 14 for Ardee. Follow N2 Monaghan/Derry. Continue on the N2 to Monaghan bypass – do not enter town. 1st roundabout follow N2 for Derry. Continue to 3rd roundabout. Take 3rd exit signposted Armagh (N12). Follow N12 for 2 miles. Turn left at signpost for Glaslough (R185). Follow road to Glaslough. 80 minutes from Dublin, 60 minutes from Belfast.

GPS coordinates
Lat: 54.31821
Long: -6.89582

Garmin Loc8 code
G6E-22-5TK

CHAPTER ONE RESTAURANT

Chapter One Restaurant is located in Dublin city centre on the north side of Parnell Square. As a former home of John Jameson, it retains authentic granite walls and sash windows and has been carefully and stylishly renovated to create a wonderfully sumptuous and comfortable restaurant.

It is one of Dublin's leading restaurants having won numerous awards for both food and service. The front of house team are warm and friendly while retaining a high level of efficiency and professionalism.

It is Dublin's premier pre-theatre dining venue. Ross Lewis and Martin Corbett, Chapter One's co-proprietors, have continued to strive for excellence and this effort is manifest throughout the restaurant. A rare treat awaits you.

Chapter One Restaurant
18/19 Parnell Square, Dublin
T +353 (0)1 873 2266
F +353 (0)1 873 2330
info@chapteronerestaurant.com
www.chapteronerestaurant.com

How to find:
Centre of Dublin – Parnell Square
is at the top of O'Connell Street.

Proprietors: Ross Lewis and Martin Corbett
Opening hours:
Lunch: Tuesday – Friday 12.30 – 2.00.
Dinner: Tuesday – Saturday 5.30 – 10.00.
Annual Holidays: Christmas – two weeks;
August – two weeks.
Private Dining: The Jameson Room: 14 people.
The Vault Room: 16 people.

CLARE ISLAND LIGHTHOUSE

The 200 year old Lighthouse, situated on Clare Island in Clew Bay Co. Mayo, has been completely restored and opened for guests in 2013. Its location high on the cliffs, 120 meters above the sea, enables a spectacular vista over the Atlantic Ocean and surrounding areas.

Our interiors, in keeping with the ethos of the Lighthouse, are understated but exceedingly comfortable.

For our guests we prepare fine food, supplemented by local produce, bursting with freshness and flavours complimented by a good selection of International wines.

Clare Island Lighthouse is one of the GREAT LIGHTHOUSES of Ireland on the Wild Atlantic Way.

Accommodation **5 bedrooms/Suites**

Specialist accommodation **Lighthouse**

Clare Island Lighthouse
T +353 (0)87 668 9758
info@clareislandlighthouse.com
bookinglighthouse@gmail.com
www.clareislandlighthouse.com

Proprietor: The Fischer Family
General Manager: Ms Roie Mc Cann
March 25th (Easter) – October 3rd.
Not suitable for children under 16
Minimum 2 night stay
€350 – €490 pps for 2 nights
includes BB and 6 course Dinner
Single supplement €100
Dogs by arrangement
Visa and MasterCard accepted.

How to find:
Directions from Westport to Clare Island –
Take the R335 to Louisburgh (20km).
Approximately 1.5km after Louisburgh town take
a right turn for Roonagh Pier (approx 7km).
The ferry sails from Roonagh Pier to Clare Island.
(20 minutes approx.).

GPS coordinates
53.82822 N
-9.98340 E

COOPERSHILL HOUSE

2 hours from Dublin in the dramatic North West, a genuine, romantic, Grand Irish Country House with comfort, character and **sublime cooking.**

A stunning mile long avenue crossing the River Unshin and winding through ancient woods and deer pastures on the 500 acre Private Estate brings you to this fabulous Georgian mansion. Coopershill has been the family home to 8 generations of O'Haras and personal attention from the owners is guaranteed.

The perfect base for exploring WB Yeats country, Lissadell House, links golf, hiking around our lakes, mountains & neolithic tombs and surfing & horse riding on empty beaches.

Awards include:
Great Taste Awards 2014 2 Gold Stars
John & Sally McKenna's 100 Best Places to Stay 2015
Andrew Harper 2013 for Hospitality

Recommended by Alistair Sawday, Georgina Campbell, Good Hotel Guide, Karen Brown, Fodor's and all good guide books.

Bedrooms **8**   Specialist accommodation **Historic House**

Coopershill House, Riverstown, Co.Sligo, F52 EC52
T +353 (0)71 916 5108
ohara@coopershill.com
www.coopershill.com

Proprietor: The O'Hara Family
Open 25 March to end of October
Open all year for house parties
Bed & Breakfast
from €99 – €109 pps low season
from €109 – €122 pps high season
Single supplement €50
4 course dinner at 8.00pm €54
Dogs and horses by arrangement.

How to find:
On N4 route to Dublin 19km south-east of Sligo. At Drumfin cross roads follow signs to Riverstown and Coopershill.

GPS coordinates
N 54.1381
W 8.4154

CURRAREVAGH HOUSE

Old fashioned (in the best sense of the word), Currarevagh is situated on the shores of Lough Corrib in 150 acres of private woodland estate, now a European Special Area of Conservation. It is run as a private country house rather than an hotel, and the tranquil informality lends itself to those seeking to escape today's hectic world.

Built by the present owner's ancestors in 1842, the exceptional food, cooked by Lucy with flair, originality and passion, and magical grounds take centre stage. Having Connemara and the Aran Islands within easy touring reach, our own boats for guest's use, many walks and abundant wildlife – it all makes a unique, original and wonderful experience not to be missed.

Recent accolades:

Tripadvisor Traveller's Choice 2015 Top 25 Small Hotels in Ireland
Tripadvisor Traveller's Choice 2014 Top 25 Small Hotels in Ireland
Good Hotel Guide Gold Award 2013

Bedrooms **12**   Guesthouse ★ ★ ★ ★

Currarevagh House, Oughterard, Connemara, Co.Galway
T +353 (0)91 552312
   +353 (0)91 552313
F +353 (0)91 552731
rooms@currarevagh.com
www.currarevagh.com

Proprietors: The Hodgson Family
Open 17 March to 31 October
Bed and Breakfast from €70.00 – €90.00 pps
Single Rooms available
Dinner €48.00

How to find:
Take the N59 (Galway/ Clifden) road to Oughterard. Turn right in village square and follow the Glann road for 4 miles (6km).

Extra information:
Reduced Half Board Rates for visits of 2 or more days. Weekly half board rate from €795 pp per week.
Out of season house parties are welcome (excluding Christmas and New Year).

GPS coordinates
N 53 27.657
W 9 21.518

DUNBRODY HOUSE

Indulgence is the order of the day at Dunbrody with world-renowned gourmet restaurant, chic champagne seafood bar and breakfast til Noon daily. Couple this foodie focus with our aim to please and pamper and you get a feel for what Dunbrody House is loved for. Set in 300 acres of parkland on the idyllic Hook Peninsula on Ireland's south coast 1830s Dunbrody really is the perfect year-round choice for a romantic getaway to the country.

For the culinary inquisitives there's the temptation of our cookery school with a range of 1, 2 & 5 day courses and for those seeking some me-time there's the luxury boutique Spa.

Tasting the craft beers from our micro-brewery and sampling of the "craic" in our traditional Irish pub "The Local" are also musts.

"Ease, Elegance, Excellence" Seamus Heaney, Poet Laureate

Bedrooms **22** including Suites and Guest Lodge   Hotel ★ ★ ★ ★

**Dunbrody Country House Hotel,
Arthurstown,Y34 R597 Co. Wexford**
T +353 (0)51 389600
F +353 (0)51 389601
info@dunbrodyhouse.com
www.dunbrodyhouse.com

Proprietors: Catherine & Kevin Dundon
B&B from €75 – €155 pps low season,
€95 – €195 pps high season
Single Supplement €25 per night on
standard double rooms
Seasonal 5 course Dinner Menu €65 and
€80 8 course Tasting Menu.

How to find:
M11/N11 from south Dublin and then the
R733 to Arthurstown.
M9 from north Dublin to New Ross and then the
R733 to Arthurstown.
N25 from Cork/Waterford and the Passage East
car ferry to Ballyhack.
FlyVLM from London Luton &
Birmingham to Waterford

ENNISCOE HOUSE

Hidden among the woods at the foot of Nephin is Enniscoe, 'the last Great House of North Mayo' overlooking the waters of Lough Conn. The estate has been in the family since the 1650s and the classical Georgian house dates from the 1790s.

The current generation, Susan Kellett and her son Dj, are happy to share their house and grounds with guests. There are elegant reception rooms and fine bedrooms with stunning views over lake and park. Outside are pastures, shrubberies, miles of woodland and lakeside walks, a carefully restored Victorian pleasure garden and an organic vegetable garden. Good food, freshly prepared, uses fruit and vegetables from the garden as well as other local produce.

Bedrooms **6**

Specialist accommodation **Historic House**

Enniscoe House, Castlehill, Ballina, Co.Mayo
T +353 (0)96 31112
F +353 (0)96 31773
mail@enniscoe.com
www.enniscoe.com

Proprietor: Susan Kellett and Dj Kellett
Open 1 April to 31 October.
Open all year for house parties.
Bed & Breakfast from €80 – €120 pps.
Dinner €50 at 7.30 – 8.00pm.
Single supplement €20.
Dogs welcome.

How to find:
Enniscoe is 3.2km south of the village of Crossmolina on the R315 to Pontoon and Castlebar. It is 20km from Ballina.

GPS coordinates
Lat: 54.07487
Long: -9.31224

GHAN HOUSE

Built in 1727, Ghan House is a listed Georgian House and Restaurant set within 3 acres of walled mature gardens.

It is just a tree length from medieval Carlingford, with its' narrow streets, town gate, castles, priory & ancient walls. Ghan House is one hour from Dublin and Belfast.

The 2 AA Rosette awarded restaurant utilises the herb & vegetable gardens and celebrates its' position on Carlingford Lough with the local seafood and Cooley mountain lamb and beef.

Whether you stay in the old house or one of the garden bedrooms, views of Carlingford Lough, the Mourne mountains or Slieve Foy come as standard.

Awards:

2 **AA** Rosettes since 2011

John & Sally McKenna's "Best 100 Places to stay in Ireland" every year since 1999

Head Chef 'Best Chef in Leinster 2015' YesChef Restaurant awards
'Alastair Sawday' recommended every year since 1999

Bedrooms **12**   Specialist accommodation **Historic House**

Ghan House, Carlingford, Co.Louth
T +353 (0)42 937 3682
info@ghanhouse.com
www.ghanhouse.com

Proprietor: Paul & Joyce Carroll
Open all year.
(Closed 24 – 26th, 31st December & 1st & 2nd January)
B&B from €80 pps – €125 pps
4 course dinner €49.50, most nights
6pm – 9.30pm
6 course midweek tasting menu €39.50
6pm to 7.45pm
Special midweek & weekend dinner & B&B breaks
All major credit cards accepted.

No service charge. Gratuities at discretion of guests.

How to find:
Take junction 18 on main Dublin to Belfast M1 to Carlingford. On the left, 10 metres after 50kph sign on entrance to Carlingford is a stone entrance & gravel drive to Ghan House.

GPS coordinates
N54°02.373' W006°11.044' /
54.04028, - 6.18417

GREGANS CASTLE

With breathtaking views across Galway Bay and idyllically situated overlooking the unique Burren landscape, this is the ultimate luxury and gourmet hideaway.

Simon and Frederieke manage this oasis of comfort and offer genuine Irish hospitality, award winning innovative cooking and elegant bedrooms free from the intrusion of televisions. Antiques, modern art, turf fires, candlelight and garden flowers add to the indulgently relaxing atmosphere.

Located on the Wild Atlantic Way and the Burren Food Trail. The ideal location from which to enjoy the Burren, Cliffs of Moher, Walking, Cycling, the Aran Islands, Horse Riding, Surfing, Sea Angling, Golf. Members of The Burren Ecotourism Network.

Awards include: **RAI** Best Chef Munster 2015, **Gold Medal Awards** Supreme Winner & Best Country House 2014; **Food & Wine Magazine** Best Restaurant & Best Chef Munster 2014; **AA** 3 Rosettes 2015; **AA** Hotel of the Year 2012, **NHA** Best Hotel Restaurant 2012.

Recommended by **Andrew Harper** and **Celebrated Experiences**.

Bedrooms **15**   Suites **6**   Hotel ★ ★ ★ ★

Gregans Castle Hotel,
The Burren, Ballyvaughan, Co.Clare
T +353 (0)65 7077005
stay@gregans.ie
www.gregans.ie

Proprietors: Simon Haden and
Frederieke McMurray
General Manager: Ken Bergin
Bed & Breakfast: €117.50 to €132.50pps.
Supplement for Superior Rooms and Suites.
Dinner from €55.00 to €85.00.
Open from February 12th to November 5th.

How to find:
On N67, 5km south of Ballyvaughan village.
Only 1 hour from Shannon Airport and 2½ hours
from Dublin.

GPS coordinates
53 04 36 79 N
9 11 11 19 W

HAYFIELD MANOR

Nestled within secluded gardens, Cork's premier 5 star hotel, Hayfield Manor provides the charm of a country house within the vibrant city of Cork. Splendid rooms and suites are classically styled and individually decorated. Guests with a penchant for exquisite food should sample the local fare showcased in the gourmet restaurant, Orchids, and in the contemporary dining space, Perrotts Garden Bistro.

Afternoon Tea is served in the luxuriously appointed Grand Lobby, The Manor Bar, The Drawing Room, The Library and on The Manor Terrace. The Beautique Spa features Elemis Spa Therapy, with pool, Jacuzzi, sauna, steam room and resident's gym. The concierge is on hand to assist you discover the unique attractions of Cork city and county

Awards include: **Georgina Campbell's** Ireland Hotel of the Year, **Fodor's** Choice Award, **AA** Irish Hotel of the Year, **RAC** Gold Ribbon Award for Excellence. **Tripadvisor** Traveller's Choice Awards- #3 Best hotel in Ireland, **Conde Nast** Reader's Choice Award.

Bedrooms **88**   Suites **4**   Hotel ★ ★ ★ ★ ★

**Hayfield Manor, Perrott Avenue,
College Road, T12 HT97, Cork City**
T +353 (0)21 484 5900
F +353 (0)21 431 6839
enquiries@hayfieldmanor.ie
www.hayfieldmanor.ie

**Proprietors: Joe and Margaret Scally
Managers: Anne-Marie Scally and
Ettienne Van Vrede**
Open all year round.
Manor Rooms: €99 pps to €190 pps.
Superior and Deluxe Rooms also available.
Suites: €245 pps to €650 pps.
Perrotts Garden Bistro: A la Carte.
Orchids: 5 course Gourmet Menu – €69 per person.
Afternoon Tea: 1.30pm – 4.30pm.

Private dining available.
Service charge of 10% on 8 people or more.
All major credit cards accepted.
Wheelchair accessible rooms available.

How to find:
6 Miles from Cork International Airport (ORK), 80
Miles from Shannon International Airport (SNN).
Hayfield Manor, located off
College Road opposite UCC.
GDS codes: Amadeus- LX ORKHMR,
Apollo/Galileo- LX 78441,
Sabre- LX 31327,
Worldspan- LX ORKHM

GPS coordinates
N 51.89102
W -8.48953

HUNTER'S HOTEL

Ireland's oldest coaching inn, in the 5th generation of the same family. Its picturesque gardens along the banks of the river Vartry provide a delightful setting for a delicious lunch, afternoon tea or a drink.

An ideal base from which to visit Mount Usher Gardens, Powerscourt, Russborough, Killruddery and Glendalough in County Wicklow, 'The Garden of Ireland'.

There are fifteen 18-hole golf courses nearby, most notably Druid's Glen and the European. Horse riding and hill walking can be arranged. Conference facilities available. Hunter's is approx. 60 minutes drive from Dublin, 30 minutes from Dun Laoghaire and 90 minutes from Rosslare.

Bedrooms **16**

Specialist accommodation **Hotel & Restaurant**

Hunter's Hotel, Newrath Bridge, Rathnew, Co.Wicklow
T +353 (0)404 40106
F +353 (0)404 40338
reception@hunters.ie
www.hunters.ie

Proprietor: Gelletlie Family
Closed 24, 25, 26 & 31 December.
Bed & Breakfast from €65 – €95 per person.
Dinner from €29.50 served 7.30pm to 8.45pm.
Lunch from €18.75 served 1.00pm to 2.40pm.
Afternoon Tea from €12.50 served from 4.00pm.
Private dining available.
No Service Charge.

How to find:
From Dublin: Take exit 15 for Ashford off the N11. Turn left at the bridge in Ashford. Then 2km.
From Wexford/Rosslare: Take exit 16 for Ashford off the N11. Pass Mount Usher Gardens. Turn right at bridge in Ashford. Then 2km.

GPS coordinates
N 53.006374
W -6.084328

ICE HOUSE

At the Ice House Hotel in Ballina, you're greeted with a wonderful fusion of old and new. 32 bedrooms and suites, all with panoramic river views, marry the beauty of the original eighteenth century building with rich contemporary styling. This eclectic mix perfectly frames the amazing views that stretch across the River Moy to the woodlands beyond.

Relax in the award winning Chill Spa with its luxurious treatment rooms, thermal suite and outdoor spa garden with riverside hot tubs and a cedar barrel sauna. Then treat yourself to fabulous food prepared by Chef Anthony Holland who celebrates the very best of everything fresh and local.

Awards:
Tatler Spa Awards 2014 – Best Boutique Spa & Best Spa Therapist
Golfers Guide to Ireland – Best Boutique Hotel 2014

Bedrooms / Suites **32**

Hotel ★ ★ ★ ★

The Ice House, The Quay, Ballina, Co.Mayo
T +353 (0)96 23500
chill@theicehouse.ie
www.theicehouse.ie

Proprietor: Pearse Farrell
Open all year round.
Closed 24 – 26 December.
Deluxe Rooms from €69 pps B&B,
Suites from €89 pps B&B.
Single Occupancy supplement €50.
Dinner: €45.
Children welcome.

How to find:
From Dublin – Follow N4/M4 route direction Sligo. At Longford follow N5 route direction Westport. Turn right onto N26 outside Swinford direction Foxford and Ballina. On arrival in Ballina, follow N59 direction Sligo through the town and across the river. Turn left at traffic lights onto Quay Road. The Ice House is located ca. 1km on The Quay.

KILLARNEY ROYAL

24

Killarney town's most charming boutique hotel. For three generations, our family has held the mantle of caring for guests at the 4 star Killarney Royal, where visitors have been welcomed for over 100 years. Committed to delivering gracious hospitality and creating outstanding memories, we and our wonderful team deliver friendly personal service and true Irish hospitality.

We provide luxurious accommodation, exceptional and innovative cuisine and, with our town centre location, the ideal abode from which to explore the bustling town of Killarney. Our door is always open and we look forward to welcoming you very soon.

Awards include:

IGTOA Boutique Golf Hotel of the Year Award
TripAdvisor Travellers Choice
Lucinda O'Sullivan's Little Black Book of 'Great Places To Stay'

Bedrooms **32**   Suites **5**   Hotel ★ ★ ★ ★

**Killarney Royal, College Street,
Killarney Town, V93 XC90, Co. Kerry**
T +353 (0)64 6631853
F +353 (0)64 6634001
reception@killarneyroyal.ie
www.killarneyroyal.ie

**Proprietors: Joe and Margaret Scally
Manager: Claire Scally**
Closed 24, 25, 26 December.
Royal Rooms: €49.50 pps to €160.00 pps.
Deluxe and Junior Suites also available
Suites: €74.50 pps to €180.00 pps
The Royal Bar & Bistro: A la Carte
The Candle Room Restaurant: €29.95 per person
Afternoon Tea for Two: €27.00 (January –
November) & €32 for Christmas Afternoon Tea
Private dining available

Service charge of 10% on 8 people or more.
All major cards accepted.

How to find:
140 meters from Killarney train station
11mi /17km From Kerry International Airport
54mi /87km From Cork International Airport
84mi /135kms From Shannon International Airport
GDS Codes: Amadeus: LM KIR170,
Galileo/Apollo: LM 38135,
Sabre: LM 060601,
WorldSpan: LM 08170

GPS coordinates
N 52.059787
W -9.506131

KING SITRIC

FISH RESTAURANT & ACCOMMODATION

Located in the picturesque fishing village of Howth, established 1971, the MacManus family have built an international reputation for warm hospitality along with fresh local seafood. Panoramic sea views, the lapping of the water, the sounds of the sea birds... only 20 minutes from Dublin Airport and 25 minutes by DART into Dublin City.

Lobster, Crab and Shrimp are caught by our local fishermen in Balscadden Bay, only metres from the restaurant and our fish is landed daily on Howth Pier. East Café Bar is open all day, with seating on the terrace.

Walking, golfing, sailing, paddle boarding, diving....Lots to do. Stay a few days!

Awards:

National Hospitality Awards overall winner "Best Seafood Restaurant 2014" – King Sitric Fish Restaurant

Georgina Campbell "Newcomer of the year 2013" Award to East Cafe Bar

---

Bedrooms **8**

Guesthouse ★ ★ ★ ★

King Sitric, Fish Restaurant & Accommodation, East Pier, Howth, Co.Dublin D13 F5C6
T +353 (0)1 832 5235
info@kingsitric.ie
www.kingsitric.ie

Proprietors: The MacManus Family
Bed & Breakfast from €65 pps
Special short breaks available
Babies and children welcome – under 12s sharing with parents free
Small dogs by arrangement
Dinner Wednesday – Saturday from 6.30pm
Sundays 1.00pm – 5.00pm
East Café Bar open every day from 10.30am
Private Dining, Weddings, Meetings, etc.

How to find:
Coming in to Howth, all the way across the harbour front to the end of the road, top of the far pier.

GPS coordinates
Latitude 53.23 18 N
Longitude 06.03 48 W

L'ECRIVAIN

This Michelin Starred Restaurant in the heart of Georgian Dublin opened its doors in 1989. This modern contemporary restaurant is run by Chef Derry Clarke and his wife Sallyanne. This Award winning Restaurant has a reputation for innovative cooking Irish/French Style, using only the best of Irish produce from small indigenous producers, all in season.

As well as our beautifully appointed Dining Room and Mezzanine Area, l'Ecrivain has two private dining rooms. The Malt Room on the ground floor seats 12 people. The Salon Privee on the first floor seats 18 comfortable and 20 max. We have a roof terrace that is a must when the sun is shining – or a smoker's paradise!

We are delighted to announce our new addition: the 'Chefs Kitchen' at l'Ecrivain. This is a separate Demonstration Kitchen where you can look and learn while you eat! For further information, please visit www.lecrivain.com

Best Chef Ireland 2015 – **Good Eating Guide**
Best Chef Dublin 2015 – **Food and Wine Awards**

---

l'Ecrivain Restaurant
109a Lower Baggot Street, Dublin 2
T +353 (0)1 661 1919
F +353 (0)1 661 0617
enquiries@lecrivain.com
www.lecrivain.com

Proprietors: Derry and Sallyanne Clarke
Extensive Wine List and Cocktail List available.
Main Restaurant seats 90.
The Malt Room – Private Dining Room seats 12.
Salon Privè – Private Dining Room seats 18.
Lunch from €25.
Dinner: 2 Course €60, 3 Course €75.
Lunch: Thursday and Friday 12.30pm to 2.00pm.
Dinner: Monday to Saturday 6.30pm to 10.30pm.
Reservations recommended.

The 100+ acre Estate offers accommodation in a style which blends contemporary design with old world charm, from the 19th Century House with adjacent Garden Mews to the Victorian Lake Lodge overlooking the beautiful Lake Abisdealy.

The culinary team in the "Restaurant at Liss Ard" will serve you exquisite food in a modern Irish style, presenting fresh, clean flavours complementing the many local food artisans of West Cork.

A magically timeless place, Liss Ard offers an ideal escape for those seeking a little time out. From the natural environment of its extensive gardens, containing the unique James Turrell "Irish Sky Garden", to the quiet solitude of its private lake, Liss Ard will remain in your thoughts long after you have returned home.

Accolades:
100 Best Wedding Venues 2015 – **One Fab Day**
Certificate of Excellence 2015 – **Trip Advisor**

Bedrooms **25**   **Luxury Country House & Estate**

Liss Ard Estate, Castletownshend Road, Skibbereen, Co.Cork
T:+353 (0)28 40000
F:+353 (0)28 40001
reservations@lissard.com
www.lissardestate.com

Rooms from €150 – €300
The 'Restaurant at Liss Ard' seats up to 100 guests, open seasonally, reservations highly recommended, à-la-carte Dinner, 3 courses, from €40
Pet friendly rooms available, dogs are very welcome

How to find:
Liss Ard is two minutes from Skibbereen town centre. From Cork Airport, follow the N71 to West Cork & Skibbereen. At Skibbereen follow the one way system to the Regal Roundabout with the LIDL Retail Shop. Take the first exit and follow the signs to Castletownshend, A596. The entrance to the Liss Ard Estate is less than 1 kilometre on the right-hand-side.

GPS coordinates
51.532348250305326
(Latitude)
-9.249801635742188
(Longitude)

LONGUEVILLE HOUSE

Set in 500 acres of wooded estate in North Co Cork, Longueville House (c1720) is a romantic Georgian Heritage Mansion owned and run by the O'Callaghan family. An ideal location for romantic breaks, private house parties, celebrations, meetings & exclusive residential wedding parties (140 Guests). Longueville offers on-site salmon & brown trout fishing on the River Blackwater, Simulated Clay Shooting, May dawn chorus Walks & Autumn Mushroom Hunts. A Walled Kitchen Garden & Working Farm, Brandy Distillery & Cider House all to explore on-site! At the heart of Longueville is The Presidents' Restaurant, with a field to fork policy offering the freshest produce from our gardens & farm with kitchen supervised by internationally commended chef/patron William O'Callaghan.

Recent Awards Include:
One Fab Day 100 Best Wedding Venues 2015, 2014, 2013
Irish Food Awards 2014, 2013 for Apple Brandy - Spirits Section
Trip Advisor Travellers Choice 2015

Bedrooms **14** Junior Suites **6**   Listed Heritage Property ★ ★ ★ ★

**Longueville House and Presidents'
Restaurant, Mallow, Co.Cork**
T +353 (0)22 47156
F +353 (0)22 47459
info@longuevillehouse.ie
www.longuevillehouse.ie

Proprietor: The O'Callaghan Family
Rates: Bed & Breakfast €90 – €130 pps. Single supplements apply. Dinner menu from €49, served 6.30 – 9.00pm. Opens Wednesday to Sunday inclusive year round. Opens for groups 20 Guests + Mon/Tues by prior arrangement. Winter opening hours more limited, consult hotel website.

How to find:
3 miles west of Mallow via the N72 road to Killarney. Take the second Ballyclough junction on the right hand side (approx. 3 miles from Mallow roundabout) and hotel entrance is 100 yards on left-hand side where a welcome awaits.

GPS coordinates
N52° 08. 308
W008° 44.188

MARLFIELD HOUSE

Marlfield is a beautifully restored charming Regency period house set on 36 acres of gardens and filled with gleaming antiques and paintings. It is situated outside the prosperous town of Gorey, well known for its boutiques and just 45 minutes south of Dublin. It's elegant and luxurious bedrooms overlook the extensive grounds and gardens.

The fine dining restaurant, housed in the Turner conservatory with frescoed walls, is highly acclaimed and open from Wednesday to Sunday. Alternatively 'The Duck' terrace restaurant, café and bar was opened in converted courtyard buildings in June 2015 and provides a popular and casual alternative serving European food for lunch and dinner daily.

Marlfield hosts exclusive use house wedding parties. Delicious food, luxurious surroundings and impeccable service provide the romantic and ultimate escape from it all.

Restaurant Association of Ireland: Best Customer Service Award in Leinster 2013, 2014, 2015
One Fab Day 100 Best Wedding Venues 2013, 2014, 2015

Bedrooms **13**   State Rooms **6**

Marlfield House, Courtown Road R742, Gorey, Co.Wexford
T +353 (0)53 94 21124
F +353 (0)53 94 21572
info@marlfieldhouse.ie
www.marlfieldhouse.com
Proprietor: The Bowe Family
General Managers: Margaret and Laura Bowe
Open 12th February to 2nd January
Open all year for weddings and special events
B&B: Bedrooms from €80 – €125 pps.
State Bedrooms: €120 – €310 pps.
Single room from €80.
Supper Menu from €36, Sunday lunch €45,
Five course dinner €65, Lunch in the garden or
Library, Monday to Saturday from €25.

How to find:
Marlfield is 75km south of Dublin off the N11 and is located just outside the town of Gorey on the Courtown Road R742. From Exit 23 on the N11 follow signs for Courtown, at Courtown Road roundabout turn left for Gorey. The hotel is less than a mile on the left hand side. From Gorey follow signs for Courtown R742, hotel is less than one mile from the town on the right.

GPS coordinates
N 52 40 06
W 06 16 46

MOY HOUSE

With breath-taking views overlooking the Atlantic Ocean, Moy House is a beautifully restored early 19th century home set on 15 acres.

A romantic 'home away from home' where a contemporary and elegant ambience is combined with warm hospitality. Nine beautifully restored individually designed bedrooms. Dinner can be enjoyed in the conservatory restaurant as the sun sets over the Atlantic.

Located minutes from world famous championships links golf courses, Moy House is a haven for the keen golfer.

Intimate venue for small weddings.

Awards include:
2 **AA** Rosettes for Culinary Excellence
Food & Wine Magazine: 'Style Award' 2012
Georgina Campbell's: 'Hideaway of the Year' 2013

Bedrooms **9**   Suites **1**   Guesthouse ★ ★ ★ ★

Moy House, Lahinch, Co.Clare
T +353 (0)65 708 2800
moyhouse@eircom.net
www.moyhouse.com

Proprietor: Antoin O'Looney
Closed November – March.
Bed and Breakfast from €92.50 – €140 pps.
Luxury Suites from €135 – €180 pps.
Special packages also available.
Gourmet Tasting Menu €60.

How to find:
Moy House is located 1km outside Lahinch on N67 Miltown Malbay Road.

Shannon airport 50km
Lahinch Golf Course 2km
Doonbeg Golf Course 28km

GPS coordinates
Lat: 52.951381
Long: -9.346285

THE MUSTARD SEED
COUNTRY HOUSE & RESTAURANT

Nestled in the heart of rolling green countryside in the Golden Vale, The Mustard Seed overlooks the rustic village of Ballingarry. On the doorstep to Adare, the restaurant is legendary with superb food and warm hospitality.

Sitting on seven acres of manicured lawns, orchard and a working kitchen garden, this eclectic, heritage hideaway is the perfect venue for family weddings, civil ceremonies and special occasions.

Close to Lough Gur, one of Ireland's finest archaeological and historical gems and surrounded by several excellent hiking and cycling routes. Adare village is a short drive. Resident Thai masseur by appointment.

"combines country house luxury with award-winning cuisine, perfect for city-slickers in need of recharging." Amie-Jo Locke, Tartler magazine.

Included in **Trip Advisor's** Hall of Fame
Onefabday 100 Best Wedding Venues 2015
'Best Customer Service' 2014 **Food & Wine Awards**
'Best Hotel Restaurant' 2014 **National Hospitality Awards**

Bedrooms **14**   Suites **3**   Hotel ★ ★ ★ ★

The Mustard Seed,
Ballingarry, Co.Limerick
T +353 (0)69 68508
mustard@indigo.ie
www.mustardseed.ie

General Manager: John Edward Joyce
B&B rates: €70 – €165 pps
Single supplement: From €25
Classic House menu: €60
Early Evening Dinner: €47
Pets by arrangement
Children welcome
Wheelchair friendly

How to find:
From Limerick: From the top of Adare village, take the N21 Killarney road for half a mile. Turn left at the first road junction to the left and follow the signposts for Ballingarry village.
From Kerry: Travel along the N21. Look for signs for Rathkeale. In Rathkeale town, follow the R518 for four miles to Ballingarry village.

GPS coordinates
Lat: 52.474672
Long: 8.864692

NEWFORGE HOUSE

Cradled in beautiful gardens and green fields, Newforge offers warm hospitality and superb food in tranquil surroundings. John and Lou Mathers opened Newforge to guests in May 2005. The light, airy rooms feature antiques and period features which blend seamlessly with contemporary comforts.

We have a passion for local, seasonal produce which John showcases in our daily dinner menu. Our vegetable garden and orchard provide homegrown produce whilst our friendly chickens lay wonderful eggs for breakfast.

Located 30 minutes drive from Belfast and near the shores of Lough Neagh, Newforge is the perfect base for exploring Northern Ireland.

Awards include: **McKenna's Guides:** Country House of the Year 2015; **Good Hotel Guide:** Cesar Award 2015; **Northern Ireland Tourism Awards** Best Place To Stay 2015; **LCN** "Best Guesthouse in Northern Ireland" 2015 & 2014; **Georgina Campbell's** "Best Country House" &"Best Breakfast in Ireland" 2014; **Good Food Ireland** "Culinary Haven" 2014; **RAI** "Best Hotel Restaurant Ulster" 2014

Bedrooms **6**   Guesthouse ★ ★ ★ ★ ★

Newforge House, 58 Newforge Road, Magheralin, Co.Armagh, BT67 0QL
T +44 (0)28 926 11255
enquiries@newforgehouse.com
www.newforgehouse.com

Proprietor: John & Louise Mathers
Open: 31 January – 21 December.
Bed & Breakfast £62.50 – £95 per person sharing.
Single supplement £20 – £30.
Special mid-week, weekend and multiple-night breaks available.
3-Course Dinner £40, served at 8pm,
Tues. – Sat. Available with 24 hour's notice.
Light meal options available on Sunday and Monday evenings.

How to find:
From Belfast: M1 West, exit 9, Moira follow 5km. In Magheralin left at Byrne's pub: left after national speed limit sign.
From Newry: A1 north towards Belfast. Follow c. 30km, exit Dromore onto B2 (Lurgan Road). Continue 8km, take right onto Newforge Road B9. Continue 1km: 200m on right after bridge.

GPS coordinates
N 54.4619 W -6.2577

NEWPORT HOUSE

COUNTRY HOUSE & RESTAURANT

A Historic Georgian House in gardens and park adjoining the town and overlooking the Newport river and quay. For two hundred years it was the home of the O'Donnells, once the Earls of Tir Connell.

Famous as an angling centre Newport House offers preserved salmon and sea trout fishing on the Newport river (8 miles) and Lough Beltra.

The cuisine is based on fresh local produce and is complemented by an extensive cellar which includes many of the classical vintages. The house is furnished with many fine antiques and paintings which provide an elegant setting for a quiet and relaxing holiday.

RAI "Best Wine Experience in Connaught" 2015.

Bedrooms **10**   Hotel ★ ★ ★ ★

Newport House, Newport, Co.Mayo   **How to find:**
T +353 (0)98 41222   In the town of Newport.
info@newporthouse.ie
www.newporthouse.ie

Proprietor: Kieran Thompson
Open 19th March to the end of October.
B&B: from €95.00 – €125.00 Low Season
        from €110.00 – €140.00 High Season.
No Single Supplement.
No Service Charge.
5 Course Dinner €65.00 also à la carte
from 7.00 pm., to last orders 9.00 p.m.

RATHMULLAN HOUSE

With its stunning location beside the sea, you will find a 2 mile sandy beach at the bottom of the beautifully maintained front garden. The interior of this country house is relaxed and welcoming with large open fires burning throughout the year.

Bedrooms range from romantic doubles with garden views to large garret rooms for whole families. An indoor pool and holistic treatments add to the relaxation.

In the Cook & Gardener restaurant, you will find fresh locally sourced produce including Donegal landed fish & seafood. The Tap Room provides an informal dining option serving homemade stone baked pizza and Rathmullan brewed Kinnegar Beer.

Awards include:
One Fab Day – Top 100 Wedding Venues 2015
John & Sally McKennas Guide – Top 100 Places to Stay 2015

Bedrooms **32**   Hotel ★ ★ ★ ★

Rathmullan House, Rathmullan, Co.Donegal

T +353 (0)74 915 8188, F +353 (0)74 915 8200
info@rathmullanhouse.com
www.rathmullanhouse.com

Proprietor: The Wheeler Family
Open full time from: March to October,
Winter Weekends, Half Terms & New Year.
B&B from €80 – €115 pps low season.
From €100 – €135 pps high season.
Single rooms available at no supplement.
Children welcome, busy with families
during holiday times.
A la carte supper and dinner available 6pm to 8:45pm
10% Service charge on extras only.

How to find:
From Letterkenny go to Ramelton (R245) and on to
Rathmullan (R247). Turn left at butchers, through
village heading north and gates are on the right.

GPS coordinates
N 55.0989383
W 7.53266

RATHSALLAGH HOUSE COUNTRY HOUSE & RESTAURANT

Converted from Queen Anne stables in 1798, Rathsallagh is a large comfortable house situated in 260 acres of peaceful parkland with a walled garden. Close to Glendalough, the Wicklow Mountains, The National Stud and the Curragh, yet Dublin Airport is less than one hour's drive.

Rathsallagh is renowned for the consistency of its restaurant over the past 30 years, showcasing Irish Country House cooking at its best.

Available for private parties and exclusive rental for all events from family celebrations, weddings, incentives to conferences and meetings catering for up to 250 guests.

Awards Include

Just Ask Restaurant of the Month February 2015
Hot Press Top 100 Restaurants Ireland 2015.
National Breakfast awards three times
Irish Country House of the Year – twice

Bedrooms **35**

**Rathsallagh House, Dunlavin,
Co.Wicklow**
T +353 (0)45 403112, F +353 (0)45 403343
info@rathsallagh.com
www.rathsallagh.com

Proprietor: The O'Flynn Family
Open all year round.
Bed & Breakfast from €95 pps. Free Wi fi.
Single Supplement from €75.
Dinner from €40.
Open for Sunday lunch.
Prior reservation essential.
Available for private fully serviced rentals.
Site inspections by appointment only.

How to find:
Signposted from Dunlavin.
Less than 50 mins Dublin airport.
M50 for Kildare / South - N7 South.
Exit jct. 11 for M9 south. Exit jct. 3 left
signposted.

RESTAURANT FORTY ONE

40

Under the expert guidance of award-winning Chef Graham Neville, Restaurant FortyOne has flourished.

Graham and his team create delicate, elegant dishes, using the finest ingredients from their very own garden in Kenah Hill, Killiney.

Looking over the beauty of Stephen's Green, the dining room of Restaurant FortyOne is an intimate and serene setting in the heart of Dublin city.

The staff, meanwhile, are attentive and mindful. This is fine-dining without the stuffiness.

Recent awards:
2013 & 2014 **Food and Wine Magazine** Best Dublin Restaurant
2013 & 2014 **Food and Wine Magazine** Best Dublin Chef
2014 **Food and Wine Magazine** Chef of the Year

Restaurant Forty One
41 St Stephen's Green, Dublin 2
T +353 (0)1 662 0000
info@restaurantfortyone.ie
www.restaurantfortyone.ie

Proprietor: Olivia Gaynor Long
Opening Hours: Tuesday – Saturday
(Lunch: 12.30pm – 2.30pm)
(Dinner: 5.30pm – 10.30pm)
Annual Holidays: First two weeks in August and
after lunch on December 24th – December 31st
for dinner

How to find:
St. Stephen's Green East, opposite the Green

RESTAURANT PATRICK GUILBAUD

Established in 1981, Restaurant Patrick Guilbaud is Ireland's top restaurant, holder of two Michelin stars as well as virtually all the top national and international awards. It is situated in an 18th century Georgian Townhouse adjoining the Merrion Hotel. It houses an impressive collection of Irish Art.

This bright, elegant restaurant, run by Stephane Robin, serves modern classic cuisine using the best Irish produce in season. Chef Guillaume Lebrun's signature dishes include the Lobster Ravioli, Roast Challans Duck, Assiette Gourmande au Chocolat.

The wine list is very impressive in both its depth and its range – do take time to peruse it.

Covers **85**

Restaurant Patrick Guilbaud,
21 Upper Merrion Street, Dublin 2
T +353 (0)1 6764 192
F +353 (0)1 6610 052
info@restaurantpatrickguilbaud.ie
www.restaurantpatrickguilbaud.ie

Proprietor: Patrick Guilbaud
Chef: Guillaume Lebrun
Manager: Stephane Robin
Open: Tuesday to Saturday.
Closed 25th December – 5th January.
Lunch: 12:30 – 2:15pm. Dinner: 7pm – 10:15pm
Lunch Menu: €45 (2 Courses) €55 (3 Courses),
except December.
Special Christmas Lunch Menu €75 for
all December.

Seasonal Tasting Menu: €98,
available only from Tuesday to Friday.
A la Carte available Lunch & Dinner.
Private Dining Room.

How to find:
Opposite Government buildings.
Merrion Street.

ROSLEAGUE MANOR

A beautifully situated Georgian house overlooking Ballinakill Bay, which has been lovingly converted into a first-class hotel with a Victorian style conservatory and delightful drawing rooms with open log fires. All of the bedrooms are individually decorated and feature fine antiques and paintings.

Set in 30 acres of secluded woodland on the ocean's edge, Rosleague is located just one mile from the Connemara National Park, an area of some 5,000 acres and just 5 minutes drive from Kylemore Abbey and it's beautiful walled gardens.

Cuisine is based on the freshest and finest of ingredients, with local seafood and Connemara lamb a specialty.

Sunday Independent – *"As such, Rosleague Manor's Summer Eden is a hard stage to beat."*

One Fab Day – *"A Dazzling Dozen, 12 fabulous new Irish Wedding Venues"*

Bedrooms **16**   Junior Suites **4**   Listed Heritage Hotel ★ ★ ★ ★

Rosleague Manor, Letterfrack, Connemara, Co.Galway
T +353 (0)95 41101
F +353 (0)95 41168
info@rosleague.com
www.rosleague.com

Proprietors: Edmund and Mark Foyle
Open: 15 March – 1 November.
B&B from €75 – €115 pps.
Single supplement €36.
2 Course Dinner €32.
5 Course Dinner €50.
Special short break rates on request.
Dog Friendly.
Exclusive residential wedding parties: 95 max.

How to find:
N59, seven miles north west from Clifden.

GPS coordinates
N 53.5514
W 9.9716

TANKARDSTOWN

A stunning 18th century Georgian house set in 80 acres of magnificent parkland, comprising superbly restored surrounding courtyards and walled gardens. Guests are offered the opportunity to experience genuine hospitality whilst enjoying the true feel of the quintessential Country House.

Situated at the heart of the Boyne Valley in the Heritage county of Meath. Tankardstown is 40 minutes from Dublin City and 30 minutes from Dublin Airport.

Stay in a main house heritage room or in a beautifully appointed court yard cottage. Enjoy simple food in our 'Cellar Restaurant' or more formal dining in our 2AA Rosette Brabazon Restaurant, located in the Tankardstown Garden Village.

Awards Include: **Georgina Campbell's** Country House of the Year 2015; **AA** Guest Accommodation of the Year 2013/2014; **Restaurants Association of Ireland'** Best Chef in Leinster 2015; **Georgina Campbell's** Atmospheric Restaurant of the Year 2015; **Lonely Planet's** Top 10 Dream Business Destination 2011

Bedrooms **7** (main house)   **7** Chic Courtyard Cottages   Specialist Accommodation/
Failte Ireland's Welcome Standard

Tankardstown House, Nr. Slane, Rathkenny, Co.Meath
T +353 (0)41 982 4621
info@tankardstown.ie
www.tankardstown.ie

Proprietor: Brian & Trish Conroy
Open all year round.
Courtyard Room: €100 – €150 pps B&B
Main House Heritage Bedroom: €315 per room B&B
Master Suite: €350 per room B&B.

How to find:
From Dublin take the M1 motorway and exit at Junction 10. Follow the signs for Slane. Continue straight through the village on N51 — **or**— Take the N2 which will bring you directly into the village of Slane. Turn left at the traffic lights and continue through the village on N51. Come to main entrance gates to Slane Castle on your left. Directly opposite, turn right, at the fork STAY LEFT, and follow straight along this road for 4km.
Signposted 'Tankardstown'.

GPS coordinates
N 53° 44' 27"
W 6° 36' 41"

THORNTON'S RESTAURANT

Located right in the centre of Dublin at the top of Dublin's main shopping street – Grafton Street – and overlooking beautiful St Stephen's Green, Thornton's Restaurant occupies the 1st Floor of the 5 Star Fitzwilliam Hotel.

A wonderful welcome awaits you in this superb Michelin starred restaurant that has won every major accolade since opening including being listed as Number 25 in the top 50 Restaurants of the World, and most recently voted Best Restaurant of the Year 2015 at the Irish Food & Wine Awards.

Kevin Thornton is widely regarded as Ireland's best chef and together with his partner Muriel and the team they look forward to welcoming you.

Thornton's Restaurant,
1st Floor, The Fitzwilliam Hotel,
128 St Stephen's Green, Dublin 2
T +353 (0)1 478 7008 (Reservations)
F +353 (0)1 478 7009
info@thorntonsrestaurant.com

Proprietor: Kevin and Muriel Thornton
Lunch Menu – 3 Course – €45
Friday & Saturday (12:30pm – 2:00pm)
Pre Theatre Menu – 3 Course – €50
Tuesday – Saturday (6:00pm – 6:30pm)
Dinner Menu – 3 Course – €75
Tuesday – Saturday (6:00pm – 9:30pm)

Tasting Menu – 5 Course – €95
Standard Wine Pairings – €65
Prestige Wine Pairings – €100
Tuesday – Saturday (6:00pm – 9:30pm)
Surprise Tasting Menu – 8 Course – €125
Standard Wine Pairings – €100
Prestige Wine Pairings – €180
*Available Upon Request

How to find:
We are located on the 1st
floor of the Fitzwilliam Hotel.

VIEWMOUNT HOUSE   COUNTRY HOUSE & RESTAURANT

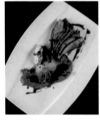

Discover this boutique gem, a secret tucked away in the heart of Ireland. This magnificent 17th century country house is complemented by its incredible countryside surroundings, and by the four acres of meticulously-maintained garden that surround it. Within the house you will find open fires, beautiful furniture, fresh flowers and Irish literature. It retains its stately, historic charm, and blends it with thoughtful renovation that incorporates modern comfort.

Enjoy Viewmount's exquisite dining experience – VM Restaurant is candlelit, with exposed stone walls, contemporary paintings, linen tablecloths. It is these aspects with the impeccable service, that create a superb atmosphere in which to relax.

Awards include:
Georgina Campbell Guide: Best Sunday Lunch 2012 & Best Restaurant 2014
RAI Awards: Best Chef Leinster - Gary O'Hanlon 2013
Mc Kenna's 100 Best to Eat & Stay

Bedrooms **12**   Guesthouse ★ ★ ★ ★

Viewmount House
Dublin Road, Longford, N39 N2X6
T + 353 (0)43 3341919
info@viewmounthouse.com
www.viewmounthouse.com

Proprietor: Beryl & James Kearney
Restaurant:
Open Wed to Sat: 6.30pm to 9.30pm
Lunch: Sunday only: 1.00pm to 4.00pm
All major credit cards accepted
Closed 24 – 26 December 2016
Closed 31 October – 8 November 2016
Bed & Breakfast: €70.00 – €100.00
5 Course Dinner: €60.00 – €70.00
Early Menu (Wed. to Fri.): €35.00 – €40.00
Lunch (Sunday only) 1.00pm – 4.00pm: €32.00

How to find:
From Dublin: Take M4 / N4 (Sligo). At the first roundabout entering Longford town, take first exit. Continue for .75km., sign for Viewmount House and VM Restaurant is on the left. Turn left at this junction). Continue for approx 800 m and entrance is on the right.
Longford town centre:
Take R393 (Ardagh), drive 1km and take the first slip road to the right, 800m, entrance is on the right.

GPS coordinates
53.72246
-7.77105

Nestled on the banks of Lough Ree, at Wineport Lodge you know you're somewhere special. Enjoy stunning summer sunsets, bold rustic food with flavours to satisfy your soul and 30 individually designed rooms & suites with private balconies and uninterrupted lake views that take your breath away.

Relaxation is what it's all about at Wineport Lodge and each of the 30 rooms and suites have been designed with individual flourishes to help you do just that. With an outdoor lakeside hot tub and intimate treatment suites, at Wineport Lodge you've got everything you could ask for and more. And all just a little more than an hour from Dublin.

Awards:

The National Hospitality Awards - Best Boutique Hotel in Ireland 2013

Critics quote - *"Dinner is an occasion at Wineport. They take food seriously, putting the same love and care into each dish as they do in creating the perfect retreat for guests."* Julianne Mooney, Travel Writer.

Bedrooms / Suites **30**   Hotel ★ ★ ★ ★

Wineport Lodge, Glasson, Athlone, Co.Westmeath
T +353 (0)90 643 9010
lodge@wineport.ie
www.wineport.ie

Proprietors: Ray Byrne and Jane English
Open all year round.
Closed 24 – 26 December.
Rooms from €69 pps B&B.
Suites from €89 pps B&B.
Early Bird Dinner: €24.95
Table d'Hôte Dinner: €49.
Sunday Lunch (4 course): €37.
Special midweek and weekend breaks available.

How to find:
Take exit 10 off M6/N6 Dublin-Galway.
Follow N55 direction Cavan. At Ballykeeran fork
left at Dog & Duck pub. Then 1.6 kilometres
(1 mile) on left hand side.

GPS coordinates
N 53.465161
W -7.884579

COOLMORE MANOR HOUSE

A luxurious early 19th century Georgian House with breath-taking ocean views overlooking Donegal Bay set on 11 acres of pasture land. An elegant yet cosy "home away from home" where a contemporary ambience is combined with antique furniture and warm hospitality.

Ideally located within walking distance to the sandy beach of Rossnowlagh. Several famous golf courses are within easy reach. Available on site are Massages, Physiotherapy, Seaweed Baths, a Hot Tub with ocean views and a Sauna. Further available on the premises: Walled flower garden, Bellavista viewpoint, Horse Riding, a small Showjumping Horse Stud and on request Lobster Dinner.

An elegant yet cosy 'home away from home' on the Wild Atlantic Way in Co. Donegal with stunning ocean views.

Bedrooms **3 double bedrooms ensuite**   Failte Ireland ★ ★ ★ ★ ★

Coolmore Manor House
Rossnowlagh, Co. Donegal
T +353 (0)71 985 9997
info@coolmoremanorhouse.com
www.coolmoremanorhouse.com

Proprietors: The Schwander Family
Self Catering. Weekly rentals.
Not suitable for children under 16.
Open all year round.
Low Season: €1,787 – €2,552
Mid Season: €1,985 – €2,835
High Season: €2,205 – €3,150
Additional separate Apartment for 1 – 2 available.
Rate includes: Heating, Electricity, Water, secure
private parking, Bedlinens, Towels, Wi-Fi, Final
Cleaning and a Welcome Aperitif.

How to find:
7km outside of Ballyshannon on the Rossnowlagh
coastal Road R231. We can send you a map with
directions prior to your journey.
From Dublin Airport: ~ 3 hours
From Belfast Airport: ~ 2,5 hours
From Knock Airport: ~ 1,5 hours
From Shannon Airport: ~ 4 hours

GPS coordinates
N 54.543194
W 08.218031

SEA VIEW HOUSE

Sea View House is a luxury holiday home located on the North West coast of Ireland in County Sligo

This peaceful and private hideaway located on Rosses Point offers guests wonderful views of Drumcliff Bay and Benbulben. Sea View is nestled in 14 acres of wild meadow, cleverly hidden away in a sheltered bay with private access to a pebbled beach.

Sea View is the perfect private retreat, promising peace and tranquillity and a blissful escape from the stresses of everyday life. The house is in a secluded & tranquil area but is easily accessed and is within 10 minutes of Sligo town.

Bedrooms **4 double ensuite,** and seperate adjoining fully contained **2 bedroom apartment**
Failte Ireland ★ ★ ★ ★ ★

**Sea View House, Rosses Lower,
Rosses Point, Co.Sligo**
T +353 (0)87 2418277
info@seaviewrentals.ie
www.seaviewrentals.ie

How to find:
Sea View is 5km from Sligo Town and 16km from Sligo Regional Airport. Detailed directions are available upon request.

Proprietor: John Lyons
Available for private rent all year around.
Rates:
High Season (July & Aug)
€3500 per week....Min 3 nights €2000
Mid Season (May & June)
€3000 per week....Min 3 nights €2000
Low Season (Jan – Apr & Sep – Dec)
€2500 per week....Min 3 nights €2000
Christmas, New Year & Easter weekly €3500
All bedrooms non-smoking.

SHANNON PRINCESS

The Shannon Princess is a luxury boutique hotel barge cruising the river Shannon in Ireland. Family run and with a professional crew, the Shannon Princess is the perfect way to explore what the river and her loughs have to offer. Guests on board will enjoy all the indulgent comforts of their own private floating luxury hotel, an unforgettable experience that will create memories forever.

Cruises are of a 6 night / 7 day duration, which can be booked by the cabin or as an exclusive Charter for up to 10 guests. Itineraries choices include Classic, Walking, Golf and Family Cruises. On board contemporary luxury seamlessly blends with a welcoming atmosphere and casual informality. Deluxe accommodations include Air Conditioning, a deck side Spa pool and delicious cuisine and wines.

Acolades: Shannon Princess is featured in **Chris Santella's book**, **Once in a Lifetime Trips** "The World's 50 most Extraordinary and Memorable Travel Experiences."
Distinctive Destinations for Discerning Travellers: *"If the Shannon Princess were land locked, it would be a Michelin Star Restaurant"*

Bedrooms **5 ensuite cabins**

Shannon Princess, Glasson, Athlone, Co Westmeath
T +353 (0)87 2514809
info@shannonprincess.com
www.shannonprincess.com

Proprietor: The Gibbons Family
Low season: April 23 – May 9. US$4,400 per person. Charter for 10 is US$41,500. Charter for 8 is US$39,300. Charter for 6 is US$37,100
High season: May 10 – Oct 4. US$5,050 per person. Charter for 10 is US$47,000. Charter for 8 is US$44,200. Charter for 6 is US$41,400

How to find:
Departures are from Glasson, Athlone to Killaloe and every second week from Killaloe to Glasson.

COME DINE WITH US

Make Business a Pleasure

Searching for an inspirational location for your next conference, corporate meeting, exhibition, gala dinner or a one-off social event or incentive? Look no further than Ireland's Blue Book.

Located throughout the island of Ireland these properties will make the perfect location for your business event.

Blue Book Gift Vouchers are an ideal Corporate Gift.

www.irelands-blue-book.ie/meetings.html / T +353 1 676 9914

Historic Hotels of Europe
www.historichotelsofeurope.com

Austria
Schlosshotels & Herrenhäuser
info@schlosshotels.co.at
www.schlosshotels.co.at

Norway
De Historiske
info@dehistoriske.no
www.dehistoriske.com

Belgium & Netherlands
Hampshire Classic Hotels
info@hampshire-hotels.com
www.hampshire-hotels.com/historic

Poland
Historic Hotels Poland
info@hhpoland.com
www.hhpoland.com

Denmark
Historic Hotels Denmark
info@historichotels.dk
www.historichotels.dk

Portugal
Hotels Heritage Lisboa
heritage.hotels@heritage.pt
www.heritage.pt

France
Symboles de France
contact@symbolesdefrance.com
www.symbolesdefrance.com

Slovakia
Historic Hotels of Slovakia
info@historichotelsofslovakia.com
www.historichotelsofslovakia.com

Greece
Yades Greek Historic Hotels
welcome@yadeshotels.gr
www.yadeshotels.gr

Sweden
Countryside Hotels
info@countrysidehotels.se
www.countrysidehotels.se

Hungary
Hungarian Castle Hotels Association
www.hungariancastlehotels.com
info@hungariancastlehotels.com

Switzerland
Swiss Historic Hotels
info@swiss-historic-hotels.com
www.swiss-historic-hotels.com

Ireland
Ireland's Blue Book
mail@irelandsbluebook.com
www.irelandsbluebook.com

Wales
Welsh Rarebits
info@rarebits.co.uk
www.rarebits.co.uk

Italy
Abitare La Storia
mailbox@abitarelastoria.it
www.abitarelastoria.it

Historic Hotels of Europe
is affiliated with

PORTFOLIO

Discovering the best for you

Trust us to find you the perfect accommodation in Southern and East Africa. When you check in at any of our establishments, all of which are personally visited by us, you can be sure that they meet our exceptional standards.

res@portfoliocollection.com
www.portfoliocollection.com

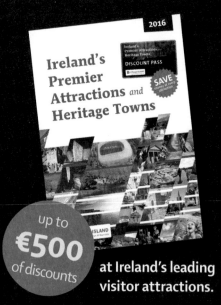

THE ULTIMATE LUXURY SHOPPING EXPERIENCE

Discover an indulgent mix of more than
60 luxury boutiques with savings of up to 60%*
and instant tax refunds on your shopping.

ANYA HINDMARCH · BROOKS BROTHERS
CATH KIDSTON · FURLA · JOULES
LULU GUINNESS · MOLTON BROWN AND MANY MORE.

KILDARE VILLAGE

#KILDAREVILLAGE

KILDARE VILLAGE IS ONE OF THE
COLLECTION OF VILLAGES IN EUROPE AND CHINA

EUROPE BICESTER VILLAGE | **LONDON** KILDARE VILLAGE | **DUBLIN** LA VALLÉE VILLAGE | **PARIS**
ERTHEIM VILLAGE | **FRANKFURT** INGOLSTADT VILLAGE | **MUNICH** MAASMECHELEN VILLAGE | **BRUSSELS**
FIDENZA VILLAGE | **MILAN** LA ROCA VILLAGE | **BARCELONA** LAS ROZAS VILLAGE | **MADRID**
CHINA SUZHOU VILLAGE | **SUZHOU** SHANGHAI VILLAGE | **SHANGHAI**
(OPENING SPRING 2016)

Enjoy one of Irelands' treasures

From horses to horticulture we offer a unique experience that can be enjoyed at your leisure or as part of a guided tour.

Come to the Stud and share with us one of Ireland's true treasures.

- Irish National Stud and Horse Museum
- World Famous Japanese Gardens • St. Fiachra's Garden
- *Located south of Dublin & the M50, off the M7, Exit 13 to R415*
  Driving time from: Shannon Airport (2hrs), Dublin Airport (1hr), Belfast Airport (2.45hrs).
  From Dublin or Dun Laoghaire Ports (1hr), from Rosslare Port (2hrs).
- Gift Shop • Open 7 days a week 9.30am - 5pm
- Contact: reservations@instourism.net or Tel: 00 353 45 521617

IRISH NATIONAL STUD
&GARDENS
Bookable on line : www.irishnationalstud.ie

HOUSE OF
WATERFORD
CRYSTAL

See Exquisite Pieces of Crystal
manufactured before your eyes

Waterford Crystal Factory and Brand Experience

The House of Waterford Crystal brings a visit to Waterford to a whole new level, as visitors can witness the creation of crystal masterpieces right before their very eyes. The factory tour is a unique and captivating experience that allows people go behind the scenes for over an hour and see exactly how Waterford Crystal pieces are made and they can witness every stage of production, from the initial design stage right up to the final engraving of the piece.

Guided Factory Tours Daily
Waterford Brand & Visitor Experience

Open Daily

Book online at **www.waterfordvisitorcentre.com** and receive a 10% discount on adult tickets

Phone +353 (0) 51 317000

www.waterfordvisitorcentre.com

The National Concert Hall of Ireland

The heart of Ireland's music

in the heart of Ireland's capital.

Be sure to drop in before you take off.

Check nch.ie for more detail

www.nch.ie
01 417 0000

NATIONAL CONCERT HALL
CEOLÁRAS NÁISIÚNTA

YOUR SOMETHING BLUE…
IRELAND'S MOST ROMANTIC WEDDING VENUES

Each house or restaurant has a reference number which relates to both the map opposite and the page on which it appears.

1. **Aherne's Townhouse**
   Tel: +353 (0)24 92424
   E-mail: info@ahernes.net

2. **Ardtara Country House & Restaurant**
   Tel: +44 (0)28 796 44490
   From Republic: 048 796 44490
   E-mail: info@ardtara.com

3. **Ballymaloe House**
   Tel: +353 (0)21 465 2531
   E-mail: res@ballymaloe.ie

4. **Barberstown Castle**
   Tel: +353 (0)1 628 8157
   E-mail: info@barberstowncastle.ie

5. **Blairscove Restaurant and Accommodation**
   Tel: +353 (0)27 61127
   E-mail: mail@blairscove.ie

6. **Browns Restaurant & Champagne Lounge**
   Tel: +44 (0)28 7134 5180
   E-mail: eat@brownsrestaurant.com

7. **Bushmills Inn**
   Tel: +44 (0)28 207 33000
   From Republic: 048 207 33000
   E-mail: mail@bushmillsinn.com

8. **Campagne Restaurant**
   Tel: +353 (0)56 777 2858
   E-mail: info@campagne.ie

9. **Carrig Country House & Restaurant**
   Tel: +353 (0)66 976 9100
   E-mail: info@carrighouse.com

10. **Cashel House Hotel**
    Tel: +353 (0)95 31001
    E-mail: sales@cashelhouse.ie

11. **Castle Durrow**
    Tel: +353 (0)57 873 6555
    E-mail: info@castledurrow.com

12 **Castle Leslie Estate**
    Tel: +353 (0)47 88100
    E-mail: info@castleleslie.com

13. **Chapter One Restaurant**
    Tel: +353 (0)1 873 2266
    E-mail: info@chapteronerestaurant.com

14. **Clare Island Lighthouse**
    Tel: +353 (0)87 668 9758
    E-mail: info@clareislandlighthouse.com

15. **Coopershill House**
    Tel: +353 (0)71 916 5108
    E-mail: ohara@coopershill.com

16. **Currarevagh House**
    Tel: +353 (0)91 552312 / 552313
    E-mail: rooms@currarevagh.com

17. **Dunbrody House**
    Tel: +353 (0)51 389600
    E-mail: info@dunbrodyhouse.com

18. **Enniscoe House**
    Tel: +353 (0)96 31112
    E-mail: mail@enniscoe.com

19. **Ghan House**
    Tel: +353 (0)42 937 3682
    E-mail: info@ghanhouse.com

20. **Gregans Castle Hotel**
    Tel: +353 (0)65 707 7005
    E-mail: stay@gregans.ie

21. **Hayfield Manor**
    Tel: +353 (0)21 484 5900
    E-mail: enquiries@hayfieldmanor.ie

22. **Hunter's Hotel**
    Tel: +353 (0)404 40106
    E-mail: reception@hunters.ie

23. **Ice House**
    Tel: +353 (0)96 23500
    E-mail: chill@theicehouse.ie

24. **Killarney Royal**
    Tel: +353 (0)64 6631853
    E-mail: reception@killarneyroyal.ie

25. **King Sitric Fish Restaurant & Accommodation**
    Tel: +353 (0)1 832 5235
    E-mail: info@kingsitric.ie

26. **L'Ecrivain Restaurant**
    Tel: +353 (0)1 661 1919
    E-mail: enquiries@lecrivain.com

27. **Liss Ard Estate**
    Tel: +353 (0)28 40000
    E-mail: reservations@lissardestate.com

28. **Longueville House**
    Tel: +353 (0)22 47156
    E-mail: info@longuevillehouse.ie

29. **Marlfield House**
    Tel: +353 (0)53 94 21124
    E-mail: info@marlfieldhouse.ie

30. **Merrion Hotel**
    Tel: +353 (0)1 603 0600
    E-mail: info@merrionhotel.com

31. **Mount Juliet Hotel & Estate**
    Tel: +353 (0)56 777 3000
    E-mail: info@mountjuliet.ie

32. **Moy House**
    Tel: +353 (0)65 708 2800
    E-mail: moyhouse@eircom.net

33. **The Mustard Seed**
    Tel: +353 (0)69 68508
    E-mail: mustard@indigo.ie

34. **Newforge House**
    Tel: +44 (0)28 926 11255
    From Republic: 048 926 11255
    E-mail: enquiries@newforgehouse.com

35. **Newport House**
    Tel: +353 (0)98 41222
    E-mail: info@newporthouse.ie

36. **No. 1 Pery Square**
    Tel: +353 (0)61 402402
    E-mail: info@oneperysquare.com

37. **Park Hotel Kenmare**
    Tel: +353 (0)64 664 1200
    E-mail: info@parkkenmare.com

38. **Rathmullan House**
    Tel: +353 (0)74 915 8188
    E-mail: info@rathmullanhouse.com

39. **Rathsallagh House**
    Tel: +353 (0)45 403112
    E-mail: info@rathsallagh.com

40. **Restaurant Forty One**
    Tel: +353 (0)1 662 0000
    E-mail: info@restaurantfortyone.ie

41. **Restaurant Patrick Guilbaud**
    Tel: +353 (0)1 6764 192
    E-mail: info@restaurantpatrickguilbaud.ie

42. **Rosleague Manor**
    Tel: +353 (0)95 41101
    E-mail: info@rosleague.com

43. **Tankardstown House**
    Tel: +353 (0)41 982 4621
    E-mail: info@tankardstown.ie

44. **Thornton's Restaurant**
    Tel: +353 (0)1 478 7008 (Reservations)
    E-mail: info@thorntonsrestaurant.com

45. **Viewmount House**
    Tel: + 353 (0)43 3341919
    E-mail: info@viewmounthouse.com

46. **Wineport Lodge**
    Tel: +353 (0)90 643 9010
    E-mail: lodge@wineport.ie